Paper Plate Phonics Book 3
Rhyming Stories

Written by: Wendy Weir
Illustrated by: Kelly McMahon
Graphic Design by: Cynthia Hoff

Table of Contents, Paper Plate Phonics - Rhyming Stories

Note to Teachers and Parents

The intention of the activities in this book is to broaden and deepen a child's reading skills. There are six stories and each story is a rhyming poem with five to eight pages. Each story concentrates on a specific sound. Sounds with more than one spelling were intentionally chosen in order to increase the child's exposure to and practice with this confusing aspect of phonics. Each story includes some words most children would not know but can be decoded. Urge the child to deduce the meaning of the word from the context and then look the word up in the dictionary to confirm the definition. The stories are intended to be read with an adult or skilled reader several times in order to learn any new words and to work out the flow of the words and the meter of the poem. By following the basic instructions a child should gain increased vocabulary, sequencing skills, meaning from context skills, phonetic decoding skills and increased confidence in reading aloud. The extended activities use each story as a beginning point for both research and writing.

General Directions For All Six Stories

1. Reproduce or remove from this book the pages required for the story desired. (Example: pages 7 through 17 for the story Tea In A Tree.)

2. Let the child color the pictures and trim the page by cutting the thick dark line around the picture and the story. Do Not Cut the broken line.

3. The adult or skilled reader should read the story through aloud the first time while the child (or children in a small group) follow along.

4. The adult or skilled reader reads the story again. This time the child should underline the KEY rhyming sound each time he hears it. Bring the child's attention to the fact that the same sound is spelled several different ways. Discuss any words the child does not know. The child may want to number the pages in the correct sequence at this time.

5. The adult or skilled reader and the child now read the story together out loud. This gives the child the feel for the flow of the words, the meter of the poem and the pronunciation of any unfamiliar words.

6. The child should practice reading until he is proficient with the entire story.

7. Follow the directions for making the paper plate "story holder" that goes with that particular story. (Example: the story holder for the Tea In A Tree is on pages 5 and 6.) Choose some of the extended activities for the child to complete.

8. The story pages can be folded along the dotted line and stored in the "story holder." The stories can be read to siblings, grandparents and peers. The listener will be impressed by skill with which the story is read and the growing vocabulary of the reader. This encourages the reader to continue reading new stories and increasing his vocabulary even further.

Directions for the Tea In A Tree Story Holder

Materials for each child:

2 paper plates
several paper clips
stapler
template for cutting the paper plate (reproduce page 6)
scissors
crayons, paint, stickers, and rubber stamps for decoration are optional

Instructions:

1. Use paper clips to attach the template to both of the paper plates. Cut around the template and remove it from the paper plates.

2. Place the two paper plates together, rim to rim, and staple around the edges leaving the top open as shown.

3. Decoration is optional at this time.

Extended Activities:

1. Use a marker to underline all the words in the story that rhyme with tea and tree. Separate them into lists by matching the spelling of the various endings.

2. Write a short poem using the same ending sound.

3. Find out more about tea; What it is, how it is grown, what are the various types of tea, and how tea is prepared.

4. In some countries "high tea" is a meal. Find out what foods "high tea" might include and what countries might serve "high tea".

5. Do some research on the tea ceremonies of Japan.

6. Taste test various kinds of tea and honey. Make a graph to show which combinations are most popular in your class.

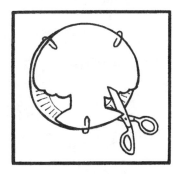
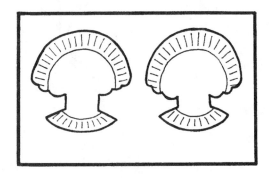
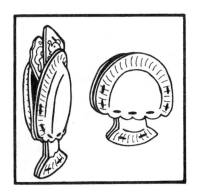

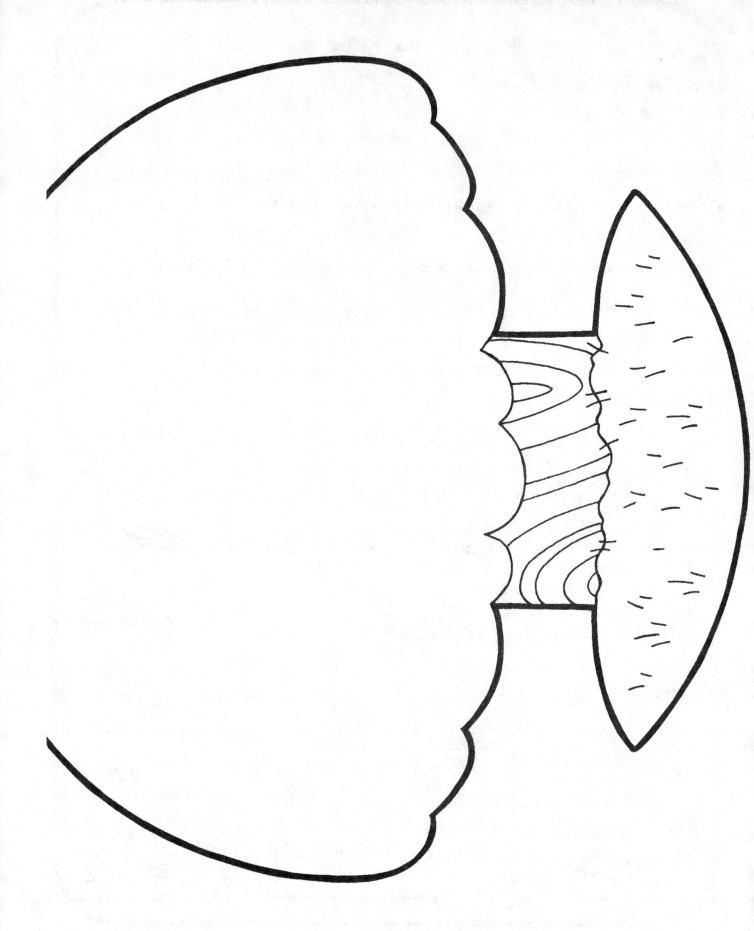

Tea In A Tree

There once lived a gigantic tree
Where the animals held their jamboree.
For one whole week they were carefree
From the big elephant to the tiny flea.

There was a monkey named Marie.
She was on a banana spree.
From branch to branch she swung with glee,
Picking bananas, one, two, three.

She bumped into Max the chimpanzee,
Who said, "Please stop and have some tea.
I've cakes and cream and a strawberry
And we can invite the old queen bee."

11

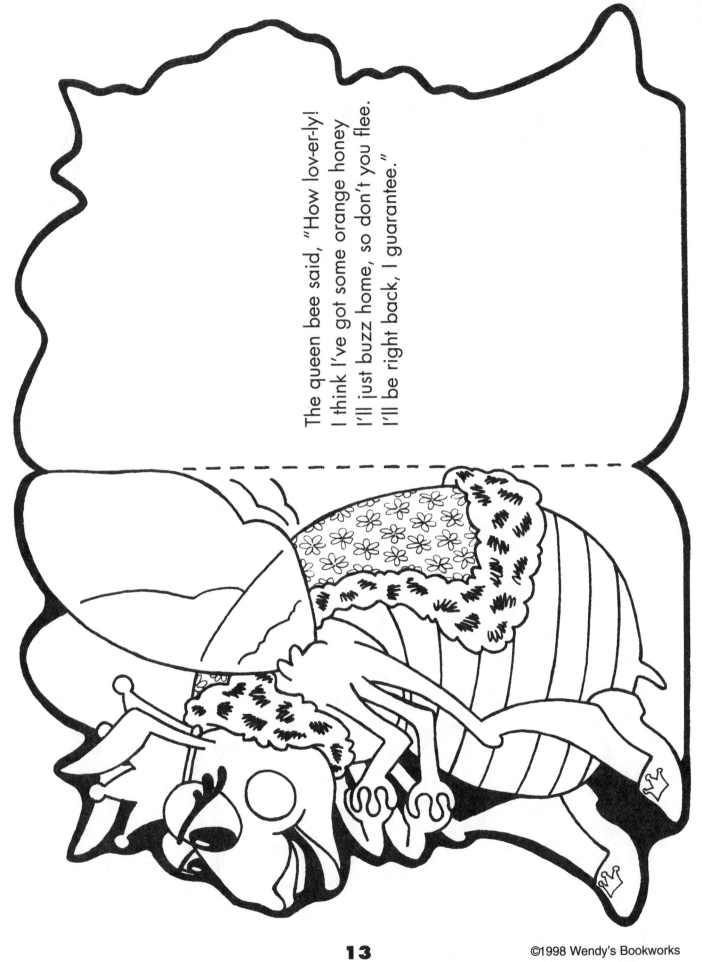

The queen bee said, "How lov-er-ly!
I think I've got some orange honey
I'll just buzz home, so don't you flee.
I'll be right back, I guarantee."

13

The hive was entwined by a giant sweet pea;
The honey under lock and key.
She grabbed the first jar she could see
And hurried back to afternoon tea.

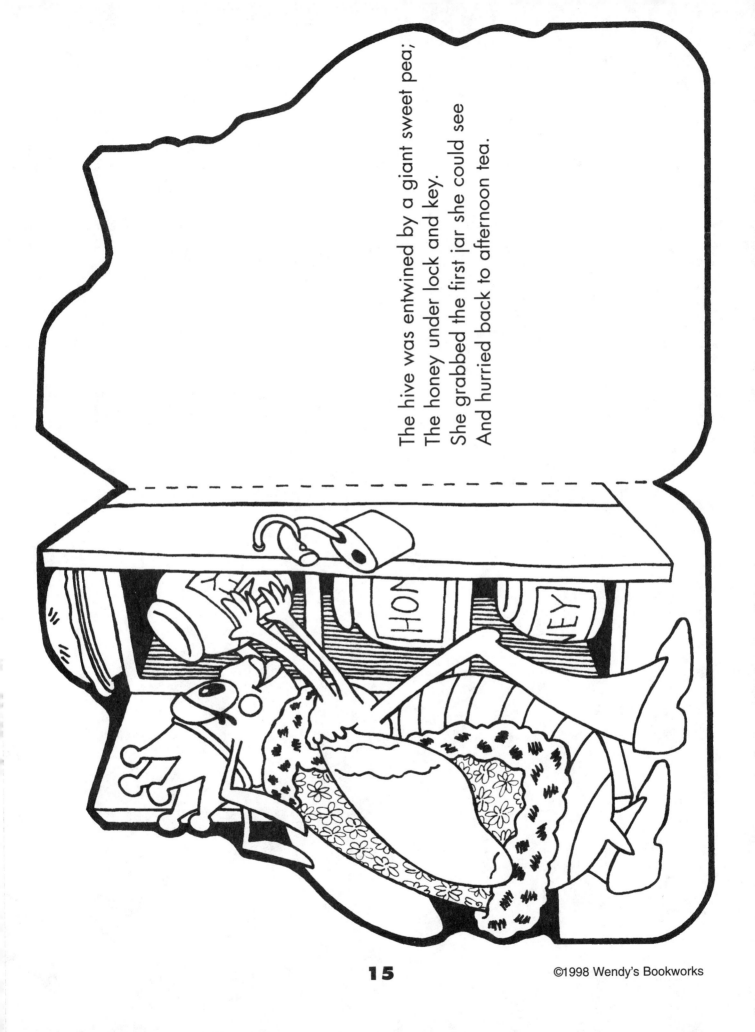

15

It was indeed a wonderful tea.
On that point they did all agree.
They ate and drank and sang off key;
The monkey, the chimp and the old queen bee.

17

Directions for the Caribou in his Canoe Holder

Materials for each child:

1 paper plate
several paper clips
stapler
template for cutting the paper plate (reproduce page 20)
scissors
crayons, paint, stickers, and rubber stamps for decoration are optional

Instructions:

1. Fold the paper plate in half. Use paper clips to attach the template to the plate.

2. Cut out the rectangle along the folded edge as shown.

3. Remove the cutting template and staple the rims of the paper plate together.

4. Decoration is optional at this time.

Extended Activities:

1. Use a marker to underline all the words in the story that rhyme with caribou and canoe.
   Separate them into lists by matching the spelling of the various endings.

2. Write a stanza of the poem for the gnu.

3. Use a map to find the places mentioned in the poem. Can you find other places that end with the ew sound?

4. Write a research report about each of the different animals in the story.

5. Put on a barbeque and talent show in your classroom.

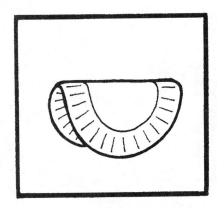  

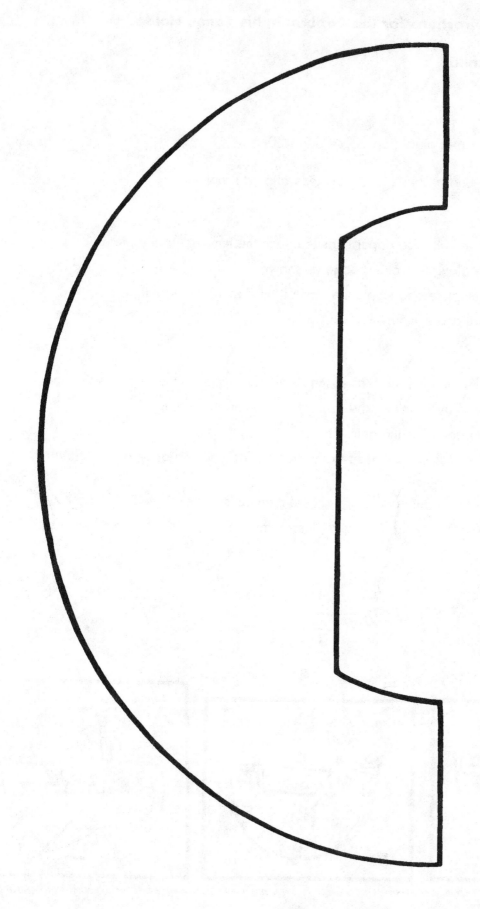

20

The Caribou And His Canoe

Through the arctic ocean blue,
Paddled Maurice the caribou
In his oilskin canoe
To rendezvous with his girlfriend Sue.

An iceberg floated into view
And on it stood a kangaroo
Dressed up like a buckaroo.

"I'm lost," he said as he sneezed, "ah-choo!
I was on my way to a barbecue!"
He lassoed the bow of the sleek canoe,
"Do you mind if I ride along with you?"

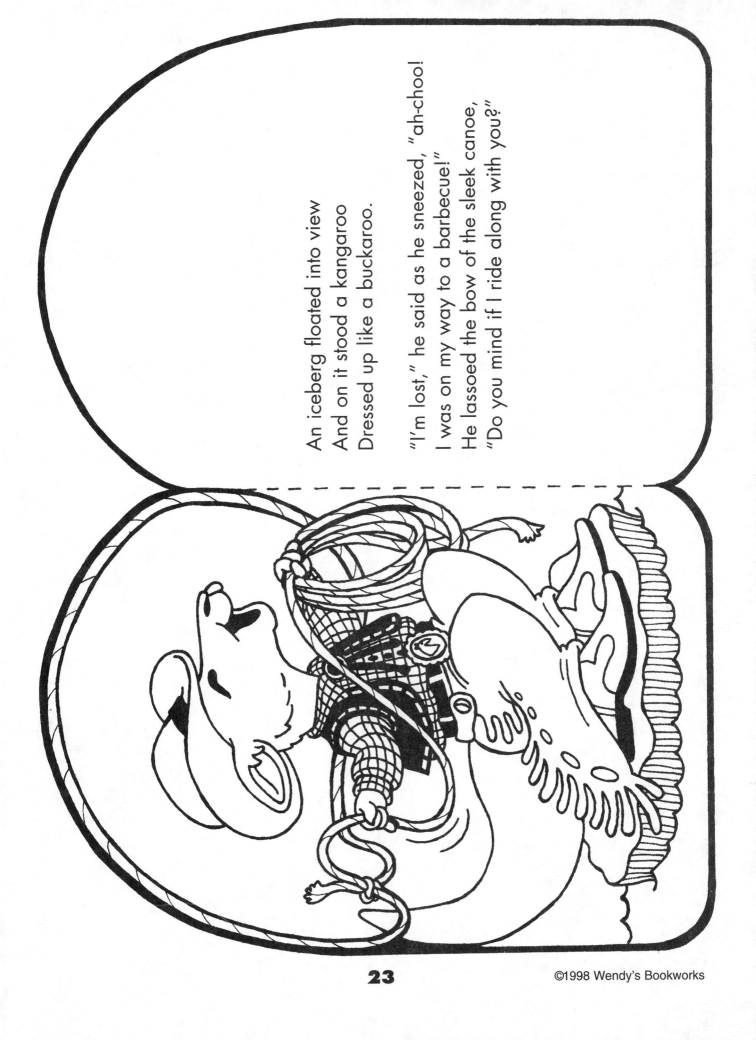

23

Maurice was about to say, "No can do."
When from above came a loud "Boohoo!"

In the sky was a floating ewe
Her parachute was her pink tutu.
She landed lightly in the canoe
And did a pirouette on her pink toe shoe.
"I really am quite overdue,
Tonight I'm making my debut. . . .
But the airline pulled a switcheroo;
I'm here instead of Timbuktu!
Do you mind if I ride along with you?"

25

"Egad!" said Maurice. "This never will do!
First a kangaroo and then an ewe..."

"And now," said a voice, "a cockatoo!
I had left Peru bound for Oahu
To buy my mom a flowered muumuu
When I hit the worst storm I've ever bee through!

For miles and days, off course I flew
Until I saw your lovely canoe.
"Do you mind if I ride along with you?"

"Oh no!" cried Maurice the caribou.
"My canoe looks like a floating zoo!
All we need now is a gnu!"

"Well," said a voice, "will a cuckoo do?
I was on the set with a movie crew,
On location in Malibu,
When the wind machine blew on — off cue.
Do you mind if I ride along with you?"

Poor Maurice was stuck, he knew.
"I'll take you all to pier number two.
Then adieu to you and I'll pick up Sue.
From there take a cab up the avenue
And catch a plane from out of the blue
Or mail yourselves home — postage due!"

29

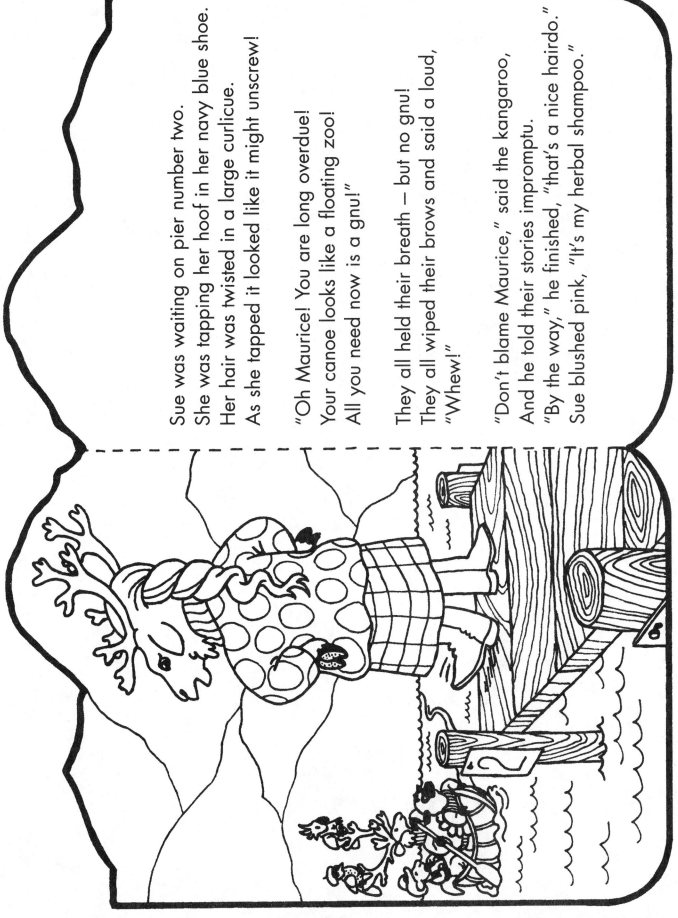

Sue was waiting on pier number two.
She was tapping her hoof in her navy blue shoe.
Her hair was twisted in a large curlicue.
As she tapped it looked like it might unscrew!

"Oh Maurice! You are long overdue!
Your canoe looks like a floating zoo!
All you need now is a gnu!"

They all held their breath — but no gnu!
They all wiped their brows and said a loud,
"Whew!"

"Don't blame Maurice," said the kangaroo,
And he told their stories impromptu.
"By the way," he finished, "that's a nice hairdo."
Sue blushed pink, "It's my herbal shampoo."

31

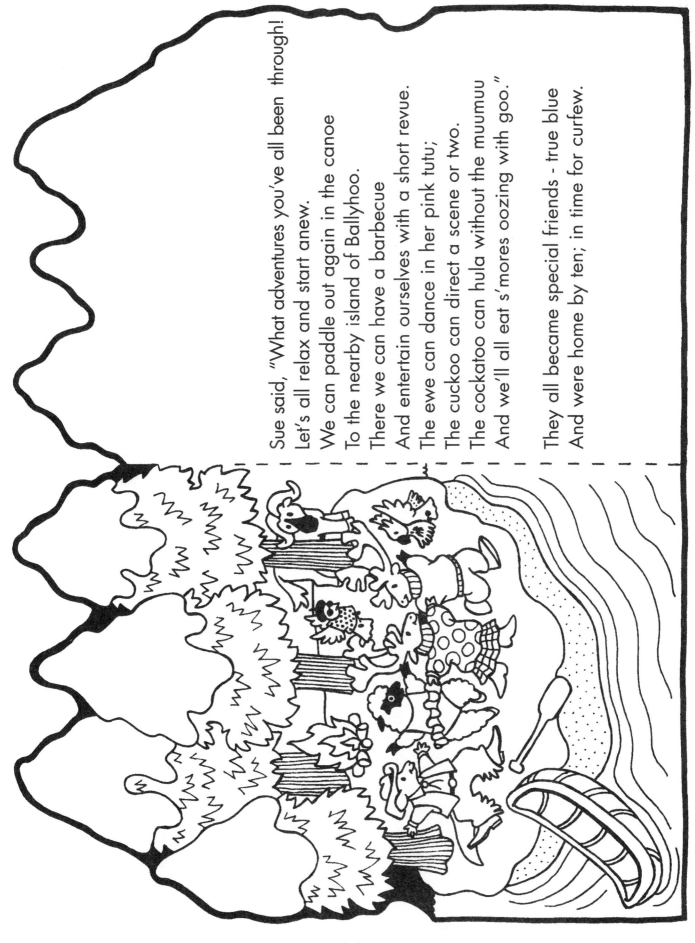

Sue said, "What adventures you've all been through!
Let's all relax and start anew.
We can paddle out again in the canoe
To the nearby island of Ballyhoo.
There we can have a barbecue
And entertain ourselves with a short revue.
The ewe can dance in her pink tutu;
The cuckoo can direct a scene or two.
The cockatoo can hula without the muumuu
And we'll all eat s'mores oozing with goo."

They all became special friends - true blue
And were home by ten; in time for curfew.

33

Directions for Abigail the Garden Snail Story Holder

Materials for each child:

2 paper plates
snail body (reproduce page 36)
stapler
scissors
crayons, yarn, markers, stickers, and rubber stamps for decoration are optional

Instructions:

1. Cut out the snail body.

2. Staple the two paper plates, facing rim to rim, one on each side of the snail body along the broken line.

3. Staple along both sides of the paper plates leaving about 6 inches open across the top.

4. Decoration is optional at this time.

Extended Activities:

1. Use a marker to underline all the words in the story that rhyme with Abigail and snail. Separate them into lists by matching the spelling of the various endings.

2. Write a song for the nightingale to sing.

3. This poem contains some homonyms (example: sail; sale). Make a list of the homonyms from the story and write out the definition for each word.

4. Find a garden snail and place it on a piece of clear plastic. How do you think it moves? Do some research on snails and learn how they move, eat and how they make their shells.

5. The snail, the rabbit and the nightingale would all be out in the garden at night. What other animals might you find in the garden at night?.

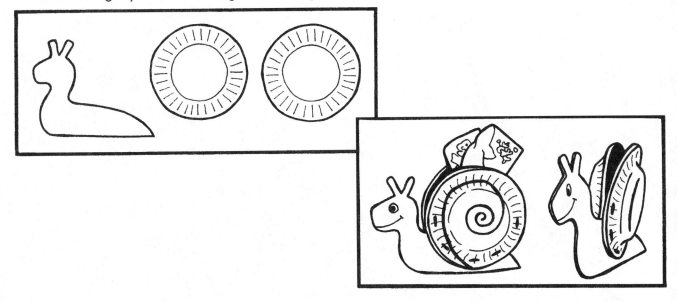

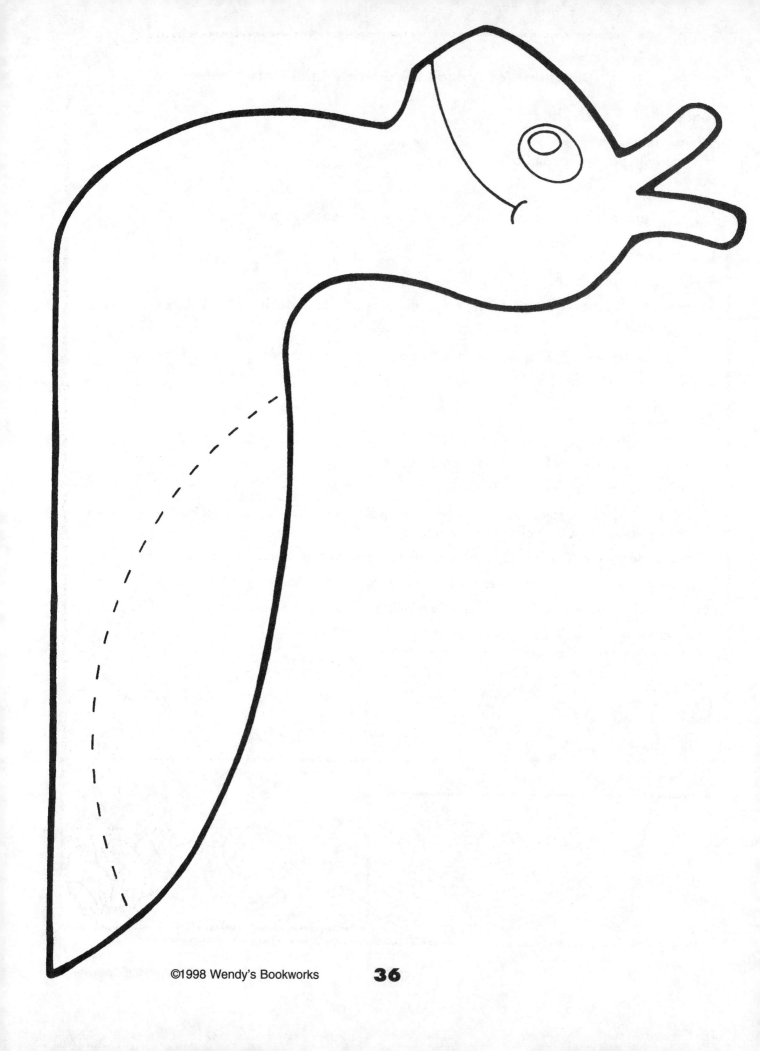

Abigail The Garden Snail

Abigail was a garden snail
Who lived inside a garden pail.
At night she roamed and left a trail
Of silvery slime in the moonlight pale.

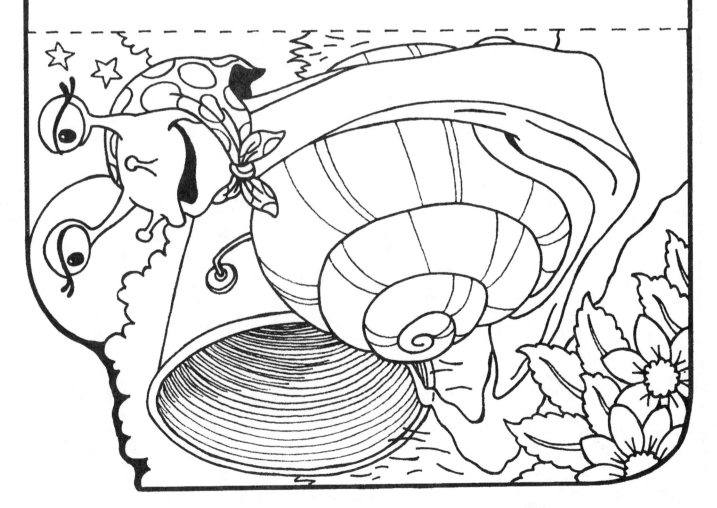

37

Her friend was Nora Nightingale
Who sang each night a fairy tale.
One of a fish with a golden scale
Another of a camel who wore a veil.

39

"What adventures!" sighed Quenten Quail.
"Around here even the jokes are stale.
Our biggest event was a rummage sale
And that was washed out by a storm of hail."

41

"I agree!" said Cathy Cottontail.
"How about a ride on a monorail
Or maybe we could take a sail
With a picnic lunch and ginger ale."

"What about a boat?" asked Abigail.
Her friends all looked at the garden pail.

43

They floated down river in the pail;
A trowel for the mast, a glove for the sail.
They were washed out to sea by a terrible gale.
They were lost. They were hungry. Quenten
started to wail!

45

"What's that racket?" spouted Wesley Whale
As he swam up to the garden pail.
"We all went for an afternoon sail
And got caught up in a terrible gale
And can't get home!" cried Quenten Quail.

47

"I can help you," said the Whale.
"Position your pail upon my tail.
I'll flip my tail and home you'll sail.
You won't need stamps to go airmail!"

49

Home through the air they did sail
And landed with a bump on a sweet hay bale.
"What an adventure!" shouted Quenten Quail.
"A whale of a tale!" sang Nora Nightingale.

51

52

Directions for the Chair Repair Bear Story Holder

Materials for each child:

2 paper plates
several paper clips
stapler
template for cutting the paper plate (reproduce page 54)
scissors
crayons, paint, stickers, and rubber stamps for decoration are optional

Instructions:

1. Use the paper clips to attach the template of the bear head to one of the paper plates. Cut around the template then remove it.

2. Attach the template to the second paper plate with paper clips. Cut around the template and cut off the ears along the broken line. Remove the template.

3. Place the two plates together, rim to rim, and staple around the edges leaving the top open as shown.

4. Option: The child may want to glue the template of the bear face to the "earless" paper plate or may prefer to draw a bear's face on the plate at this time.

5. Other decoration is optional at this time.

Extended Activities:

1. Use a marker to underline all the words in the story that rhyme with chair and bear. Separate them into lists by matching the spelling of the various endings.

2. Write a new poem for Theodore telling how he invented another type of chair..

3. This poem contains some homonyms (example:pear; pair). Make a list of the homonyms in the story and write a definition for each word.

4. Use catalogs, magazines and newspapers to find different kinds of chairs. How many did you find?.

5. Do some research to discover when people started to use chairs and furniture. Are there still some cultures around the world that prefer not to use chairs?

 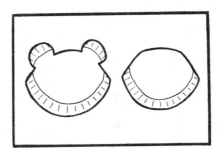 

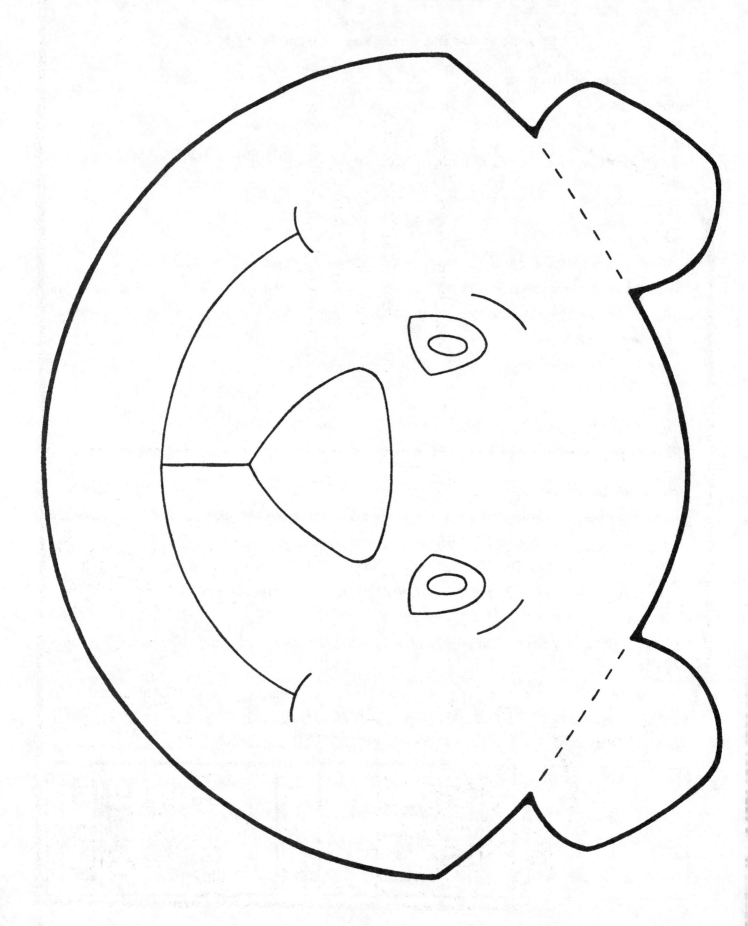

54

The Chair Repair Bear

Theodore Bear does chair repair.
He is not very debonair.
In fact he is a bit threadbare.
His sign reads, I Repair With Care.

55

It all began with his son and heir
Who, when he sat in his dining chair,
Couldn't reach the silverware.
So with some wood he had to spare
He lengthened the legs of the dining chair.
His son now perched up in the air.
Theodore had invented the first high chair.

57

He had a friend called Harry Hare
Who actually had no hair to spare.
Lack of stuffing did impair
His legs from going anywhere.
He sat in a chair at the top of the stair
And out the window he did stare
Wishing he could go everywhere.
Theodore had inside his lair
A worn out bike in disrepair.
He attached the wheels to Harry's chair.
Now Harry's doing wheelies in Times Square
In his cool new wheel chair.

There was a fat cat billionaire
Who was down and out - without bus fare.
All he had left was his office chair
And the leather upholstery had a tear.
It was brought to Theodore for repair.
He removed the stuffing, which is where
He found a diamond solitaire.
His new good fortune, the cat did share,
Then moved uptown - back to Bel-Air
And bought a brand new office chair.

61

Theodore had a friend - Pierre
Who sold fruit at the county fair.
To visit, Theodore paid the fare
To ride a cart pulled by a mare.
"One pear, two pears, makes a pair;
That's fifty cents please," said Pierre.

Pierre often sat on a wooden square
Surrounded by fruit stacked high in the air.
"You need more room here," said the bear,
"I'll fix you up with a special chair."
He took the sides off the wooden square.
He put a hinge here; he put a hinge there.
Pierre now sits in his folding chair
While selling fruit at the county fair.

63

Theodore got a call from Delaware.
It was a sailor in despair.
His sleep on land was a long nightmare.

At sea his hammock swung in midair
And rocked him to sleep without a care.
On land he lay still and said a prayer
"Someone please save me from intensive care!"

A barrel hoop was cut to prepare
A pair of rockers for his chair.
The sailor's snores at night now blare
As he sleeps and dreams in his rocking chair.

65

When Theodore had a moment to spare
He sat upon his wooden chair.
It was poky everywhere
And made him painfully aware
Of all his aches; some here, some there.
So he packed it with pillows everywhere.
Fabric covered the chair with flair.
Now Theodore sits in his overstuffed chair.
His sign reads I Repair With Care.

I REPAIR WITH CARE

Directions for the Balloon to the Moon Story Holder

Materials for each child:

2 paper plates
several paper clips
stapler
template for cutting the paper plate (reproduce page 70)
scissors
crayons, paint, stickers, and rubber stamps for decoration are optional

Instructions:

1. Use paper clips to attach the moon template to the *bottom side* of one of the paper plates. Cut around the template. The child may wish to glue the moon face to the paper plate or prefer to draw the moon face on the plate at this time.

2. Use paint or crayon to decorate at least half of the *top side* of the second paper plate to look like the night sky.

3. Place the two paper plates together, rim to rim. The moon face should be on the left and the night sky showing on the right. Staple together around the edges as shown.

4. Further decoration is optional at this time.

Extended Activities:

1. Use a marker to underline all the words in the story that rhyme with moon and tune. Separate them into lists by matching the spelling of the various endings.

2. Write an entire song for the moon to sing.

3. Do some research to learn about some of the myths and legends about the moon. Write a modern myth about the moon.

4. Do you think the moon will be colonized in your lifetime? Write about how you think that might be accomplished.

5. Jules Verne wrote "Around the World in 80 Days". How does that compare to modern day hot air balloon travel. What other "science fiction" did Jules Verne write that became reality?

6. Do some research to learn more about the luna moth. Write a legend about the moth incorporating what you have learned.

 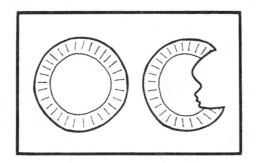 

70

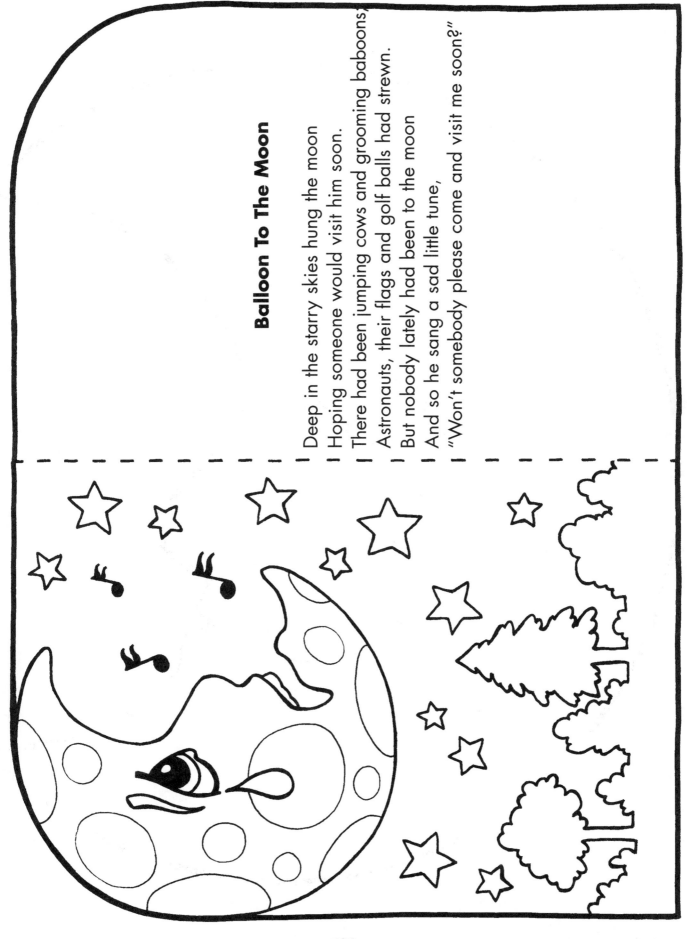

Balloon To The Moon

Deep in the starry skies hung the moon
Hoping someone would visit him soon.
There had been jumping cows and grooming baboons,
Astronauts, their flags and golf balls had strewn.
But nobody lately had been to the moon
And so he sang a sad little tune,
"Won't somebody please come and visit me soon?"

By the lagoon sat Ronnie Raccoon
Washing his spoon by the light of the moon.
The trees echoed and whispered the moon's little tune.
"Won't somebody please come and visit me soon?"

73

Along the shore paddled Lennie the Loon.
He also had heard the sad little tune.
"Let's go and visit the man in the moon!"

"Can you fly us both there?" asked Ronnie Raccoon.

"It's too far for me to fly," said the loon,
"What we really need is a hot air balloon.
There's one at the carnival opening soon
Across the lagoon - there on the sand dune."

75

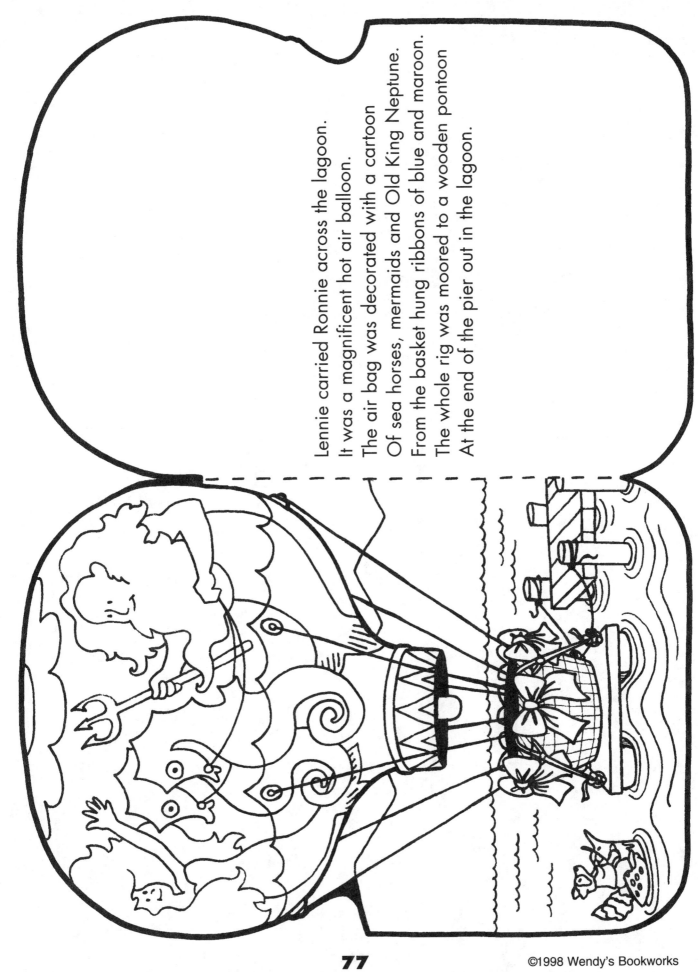

Lennie carried Ronnie across the lagoon.
It was a magnificent hot air balloon.
The air bag was decorated with a cartoon
Of sea horses, mermaids and Old King Neptune.
From the basket hung ribbons of blue and maroon.
The whole rig was moored to a wooden pontoon
At the end of the pier out in the lagoon.

77

Through the air again came the tune.
This time it was played on a silver bassoon.
There in the basket stood Bernie Baboon
"Yeah man," said Bernie "I too heard the tune.
I'd like to go visit the man in the moon
But can we return here any time soon?
How do you get a balloon down from the moon?
Could we possibly pop it with a harpoon?"

"No! The air would whoosh out like a giant typhoon!
We'd blow off course and land in Rangoon.
We wouldn't be back here any time soon;
There must be a better way." said the loon.

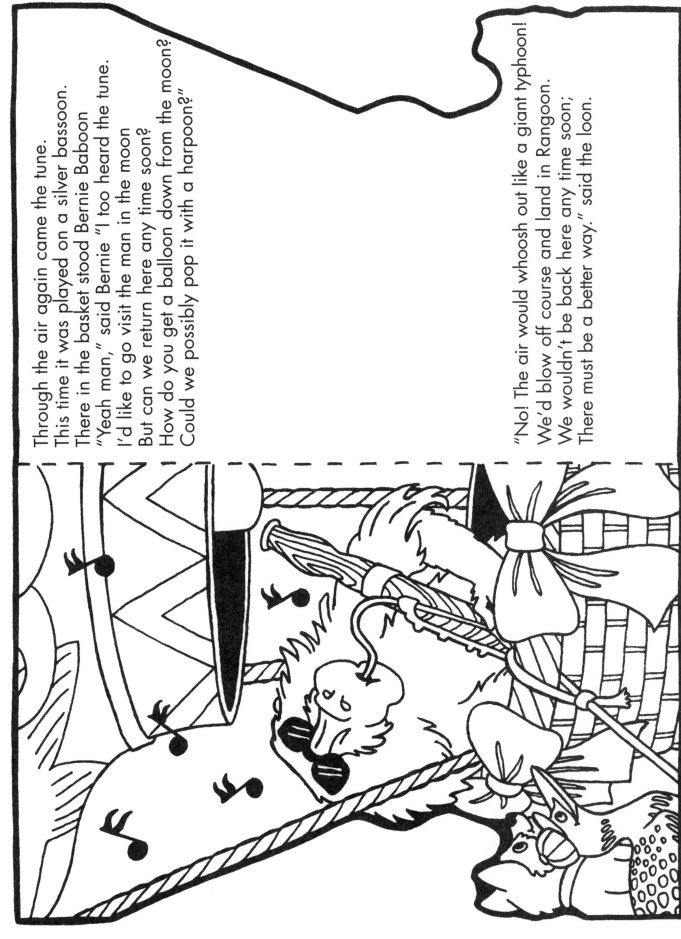

"Wait a minute!" said the baboon,
"The luna moth living here has a cocoon.
Dr. Dolittle rode a moth back from the moon.
It will find it's way home if it's mother will croon
A lullaby, which is how they commune."

Into the night rose the hot air balloon.
It's anchor caught on the tip of the moon.
They all had cheese and a macaroon
And sang along with the baboon's bassoon.
The luna moth hatched from it's cocoon;
They all climbed aboard. It's mom started to croon.

"Thanks for coming!" called the man in the moon.
"Come again and visit me soon!"
The moth landed neatly on the lagoon
In time for the carnival's first show at noon.

83

Directions for the Songs of the Troubadour Story Holder

Materials for each child:

3 paper plates
several paper clips
stapler
template for cutting the paper plate (reproduce page 86)
scissors
crayons, paint, stickers, and rubber stamps for decoration are optional

Instructions:

1. Use paper clips to attach the banjo neck template to the paper plate. Cut around the template then remove it.

2. Trim two to three inches off the second paper plate as shown.

3. Place the second paper plate and the third paper plate (whole) together rim to rim as shown. Staple the plates together around the edges.

4. Attach the banjo neck to the back of the whole paper plate with staples as shown.

5. The child may want to draw strings on the banjo and the neck or perhaps glue on some yarn to look like strings. Other decoration is optional at this time.

Extended Activities:

1. Use a marker to underline all the words in the story that rhyme with door and more. Separate them into lists by matching the spelling of the various endings.

2. Write some more songs with different rhyme endings for the troubadour to sing.

3. Write a song for an endangered species.

4. Do some research about troubadours. During what era in history were they most popular and what was their role in society? What instrument did a troubadour usually use?

5. Invite a banjo player into class to talk about the banjo, it's history as an instrument and how it is made. Are there any modern day troubadours?

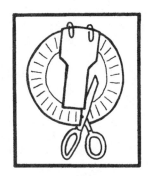 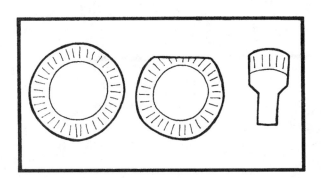 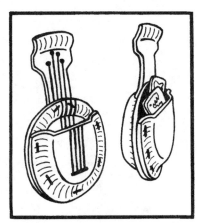

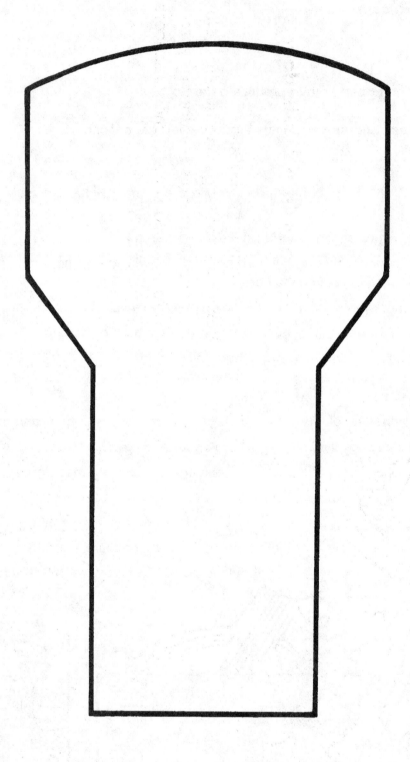

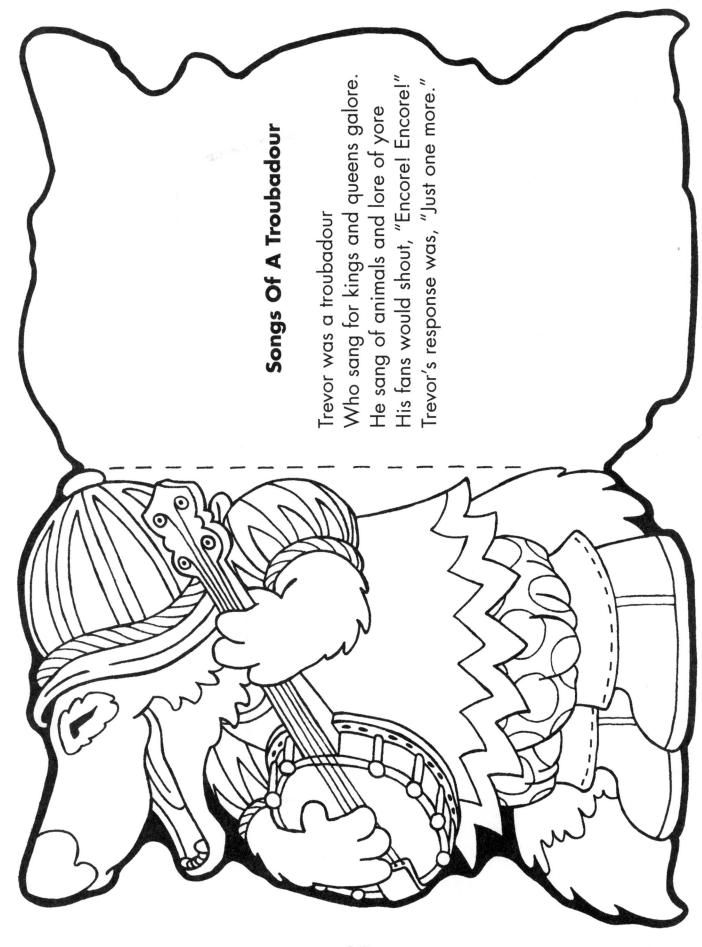

Songs Of A Troubadour

Trevor was a troubadour
Who sang for kings and queens galore.
He sang of animals and lore of yore
His fans would shout, "Encore! Encore!"
Trevor's response was, "Just one more."

87

"Here is a song of a dinosaur
Who hated being a carnivore.
He didn't like the blood and gore,
It made his stomach burp and roar.
He nibbled grasses at the shore
And now and then an apple core.
He vowed to eat plants evermore
And became an herbivorous dinosaur."

Trevor's fans shouted, "Encore! Encore!"
Trevor's response was, "Just one more."

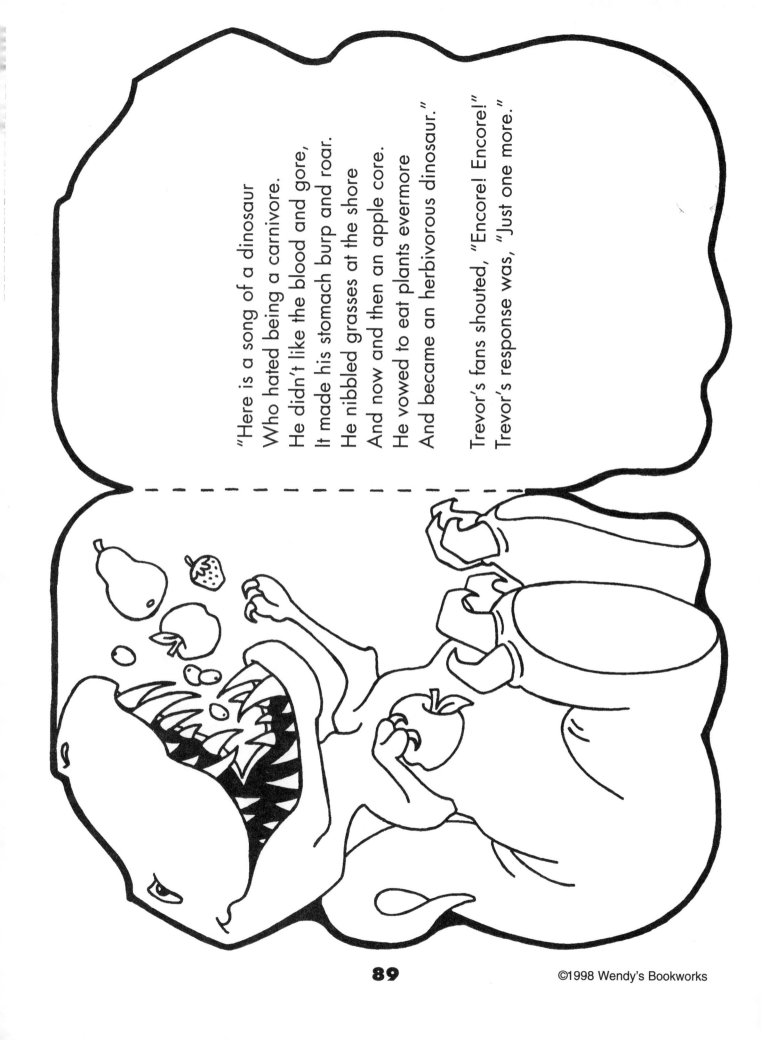

89

Trevor sang, "Now let's explore
A species almost nevermore.
For years cracked eggs were all they bore.
We almost lost the great condor.
But scientists, an entire corps,
Gathered eggs to hatch in a special drawer.
Only mothers could adore
The faces hatched, all red and sore.
Scientists danced in the corridor
And once again wild condors soar."

Trevor's fans shouted, "Encore! Encore!"
Trevor's response was, "Just one more."

91

"Jose was a matador.
Inside the ring he knew the score
Until one fight in Ecuador,
A great black bull upon him bore.

The bull passed by and through the roar
Jose heard, "Pssst! Hey senor!
Don't kill me now I do implore!"
A bull that talked to a matador
Was something Jose could not ignore.
"Tell your story por favor.
Quick, before they yell for more!"

"I was with the circus right next door
When kidnappers hit me with a two by four.
The circus moved on to Singapore
But I awoke in this ring with a matador!"

Jose waved his cape while he tried to explore
The ground to find a special trapdoor.
Jose and the bull jumped through before
The crowd could cause a big uproar.
"These unethical ways I do abhor.
I'll not fight bulls forevermore!"

The bull, his family and the ex-matador
Now live on a farm in Baltimore."

93

94

"Lucky was a Labrador.
A mascot of the Marine Corps
Who lived out by the reservoir.
He tried his darndest to ignore
The awful secret that he bore:
Anything wet he did abhor!

A dog named Sheila was his amour.
She and her mistress sailed o'er
The waters of the reservoir.
One day there came a great downpour.
A gale blew, their sail tore.
They tried to paddle and lost an oar.
They might be lost forevermore!

Lucky cringed and left the shore.
He swam out in the reservoir
And grabbed the collar Sheila wore.
Her mistress grabbed the labrador.
Lucky pulled them both ashore
And now with water he has rapport."

Trevor's fans shouted, "Encore! Encore!"
Trevor said, "Sorry, that's all. Ten-four!"

95